A *Doonesbury* Book

Bravo For Life's Little Ironies

by G. B. Trudeau

POPULAR LIBRARY • NEW YORK

All POPULAR LIBRARY books are carefully selected by the POPULAR LIBRARY Editorial Board and represent titles by the world's greatest authors.

POPULAR LIBRARY EDITION

Library of Congress Catalog Card Number: 72–91561

Reprinted by arrangement with Holt, Rinehart and Winston, Inc.

The cartoons in this book have appeared in newspapers in the United States and abroad under the auspices of Universal Press Syndicate

PRINTED IN THE UNITED STATES OF AMERICA

MIKE, WHAT'S COLLEGE REALLY LIKE FOR YOU?

OH, YOU KNOW, THE USUAL GREAT TIMES. I GO TO LOTS OF GAY, MAD PARTIES— MEET STRINGS OF BEAUTIFUL WOMEN, MANY OF WHOM ADMIRE ME.

NO, SERIOUSLY.
GBTrudeau

HEY, BENJY, WHERE'S MOM?

SHE WASN'T FEELING SO GOOD THIS MORNING, SO I TOLD HER I'D MAKE BREAKFAST.

I MADE YOUR FAVORITE, SCRAMBLED EGGS!

BACON?
SCRAMBLED EGGS?

O.K., YOU CAN STAY UP, BUT YOU'VE GOT TO PROMISE YOU'LL GO TO BED AS SOON AS IT'S OVER.
O.K.

OH, BOY! JUST IN TIME FOR THE GOOD PART!! HERE SHE COMES...

THE SWEATER!!

BENJY REALLY DIGS LANA TURNER MOVIES.

WHAT'RE YOU GOING TO DO WITH THE MONEY YOU GOT FOR CHRISTMAS, BENJY?
SAVE IT. I WANT TO GO TO HARVARD MEDICAL SCHOOL ONE DAY.

ALL THE GUYS IN MY SCIENCE CLASS ARE GOING TO HARVARD MED. SCHOOL. WE'RE PLANNING TO OPEN A CLINIC IN SOUTHAMPTON AND MAKE FIVE OR SIX MILLION DOLLARS. THEN WE'RE GOING TO RETIRE AND START A COMMUNE IN THE BARBADOS.

BIG PLANS...
YOU BET. BUT WE'RE QUITE SERIOUS ABOUT IT.

WE TALK ABOUT IT OVER MILK AND COOKIES EVERY MORNING...
I SEE.
GBTrudeau

Application for Harvard Medical School
Part I.
Date: JAN. 1

Name: Benjy P. Doonesbury
Sex: Boy

Present Educational
Status: 3Rd GrAde

ACTUALLY, THERE'S NO REAL RUSH ON THIS.
GBTrudeau

I CALLED THE DEAN OF THE HARVARD MEDICAL SCHOOL TODAY...
YOU WHAT?

HE WAS VERY UNCO-OPERATIVE. HE ASKED ME HOW OLD I WAS, AND THEN HE LAUGHED AND TOLD ME TO CALL BACK IN FOURTEEN YEARS.

"FOURTEEN YEARS"... PRETTY FUNNY GUY, HUH?

I'M NOT SO SURE THE HARVARD MEDICAL SCHOOL IS MY KIND OF PEOPLE...

I'M SURE THAT'S HOW HE DID IT!
WELL, YOU CAN ASK HIM YOURSELF, DIDI. HERE HE COMES.

SAY, MICHAEL, DID YOUR FATHER ATTEND THIS SCHOOL?
SURE. CLASS OF '46.

AHA!

I KNEW IT, I KNEW IT!
WE WERE WONDERING HOW YOU GOT IN.
GBTrudeau

HEY, MARK, I'D LIKE YOU TO MEET SOMEONE... THIS IS THE GUY WHO'S STARTED THIS NEW COFFEEHOUSE

ER, HI.
REVEREND SCOT SLOAN'S THE NAME, SON! I'M THE FIGHTING YOUNG PRIEST WHO CAN TALK TO THE YOUNG.

FIGHTING YOUNG PRIEST?
SURE, MAN. DIDN'T YOU READ ABOUT ME IN "LOOK"? BIRMINGHAM, SELMA, CHICAGO '68, WASHINGTON '67...?

OH, THAT FIGHTING YOUNG PRIEST.
RIGHT. NOW, CAN I LAY SOME JAVA ON YOU?
GBTrudeau

MICHAEL, FROM THE LOOKS OF THINGS SO FAR, I THINK MY COFFEEHOUSE HERE IS GOING TO CATCH, IT'S GOING TO GO!

IT'S JUST A HUNCH, SEE, BUT I CAN'T HELP FEELING YOU YOUTHS NEED SOMEPLACE TO COME WHEN YOU FEEL LIKE RELAXING. THIS COFFEE-HOUSE CAN BE THE PERFECT MILIEU. DYNAMIC, EXCITING, NOW.

...AND THE GOOD LORD WILLING, PERHAPS IT WILL EVEN TURN A PROFIT...
WHAT ARE YOU GOING TO USE THE PROFITS FOR?

TO WIPE OUT POVERTY, HUNGER, HATE, WAR, FRUSTRATION AND INADEQUATE HOUSING.
OH.

GOOD MORNING, BROTHER! WELCOME TO "THE EXIT," THE COFFEEHOUSE WHERE PEOPLE CAN REALLY RELATE!

REVEREND SCOT SLOAN'S THE NAME. PERHAPS YOU READ ABOUT ME IN "LOOK." I'M THE FIGHTING YOUNG PRIEST WHO CAN TALK TO THE YOUNG.

MY SPECIALTY, OF COURSE, IS SETTING UP DIALOGUES. OFTEN I AM SUCCESSFUL IN GETTING PEOPLE TO LOOK AT THEMSELVES HONESTLY AND MEANINGFULLY.
GOOD FOR YOU, SWEETHEART. ONE BLACK COFFEE TO GO.
©GBTrudeau

I MUST SAY, REVEREND, I DON'T KNOW WHY YOU DO THIS, BUT I SURE APPRECIATE THE FREE BREAKFAST...
WELL, RUFUS, I AM DEEPLY GRATIFIED.

YESSIR. THIS SURE IS A DELICIOUS BREAKFAST. ONE OF THE BEST...
IT'S PART OF MY FREE BREAKFAST PROGRAM FOR GHETTO KIDS

YESSIR, THIS IS GREAT PORRIDGE! AND I DON'T EVEN MIND THE SLIGHT PATRONIZING FLAVOR IT HAS...

HIT A NERVE, REVEREND?
SHUT UP AND EAT, YOU LITTLE PAGAN.
©BTrudeau

AH, READING THE BIBLE, EH, RUFUS?
UH-HUH

IT WARMS MY HEART TO SEE A YOUNG MAN WHO FINDS RELEVANCE IN THE BIBLE. I MYSELF FIND IT INSPIRATIONAL TO READ OF THE GREAT MEN AMONG THE LORD'S CHOSEN PEOPLE.

DAVID, JOB, ABRAHAM, MOSES... WHY, THE LIST IS ENDLESS!... SAY, WHO ARE YOUR FAVORITE CHARACTERS IN THE BIBLE, RUFUS?

THE PHILISTINES.

WE'RE IN LUCK, CHOU! HERE COME SOME FRIENDS OF MINE...

RAY, BERNIE, BOOPSIE, I'D LIKE YOU TO MEET CHOU FU LING... HE'S A NEW CHINESE EXCHANGE STUDENT!

CHINESE!!
WOW!! SAY SOMETHING IN CHINESE!
WANNA PLAY PING PONG?
YEAH!
YOU'RE VERY IN THIS YEAR...

I WISH YOU COULD VISIT CHINA, MIKE. I THINK YOU'D BE ASTOUNDED HOW WELL 800 MILLION PEOPLE CAN WORK TOGETHER
YEAH, PROBABLY.

HOLD IT, HOLD IT RIGHT THERE, FELLA! LET'S NOT PAINT SUCH A ROSY PICTURE!!

THERE AREN'T 800 MILLION PEOPLE IN CHINA – THERE ARE 800 MILLION COMMUNISTS!

THERE'S A BIG DIFFERENCE!
WHO'S HE?
NO IDEA.
GBTrudeau

YOU KNOW, CHOU, ONE THING I HAVE TO HAND YOU CHINESE –YOU SURE CAN COOK!

TAKE SUKIYAKI FOR INSTANCE! BOY, CAN THOSE CHINESE COOK SUKIYAKI!

SUKIYAKI IS OF JAPANESE ORIGIN, NOT CHINESE!
CHINESE, JAPANESE, WHAT'S THE DIFFERENCE...

YESSIR, SUKIYAKI IS ONE OF MY ALL-TIME FAVORITES.
GBTrudeau

B.D., MIKE TELLS ME YOU SUPPORT THE CURRENT U.S. FOREIGN POLICY.
DARN RIGHT, I DO!

REALLY? WHAT BENEFITS DO YOU THINK U.S. INTRUSION HAS BROUGHT THE VIETNAMESE PEOPLE?
WHAT A DUMB QUESTION! WHY, WE'RE DOING GREAT THINGS FOR THOSE PEOPLE DEMOCRACYWISE. FOR EXAMPLE, THEY NOW HAVE FREE ELECTIONS!

HEE, HEE,
HEE!!

HA, HA!
HA, HA,
HA, HA,
HA!
O.K., LET ME
USE ANOTHER
EXAMPLE.
©GBTrudeau

WOW! WHAT A PRETTY DAY!

IT'S A GREAT, BIG, SNOWY, MARSHMALLOW, FLUFFY, PINK, COTTON CANDY AND SUN-SHINE KIND OF DAY!

HEE-HEE... BUT THAT'S SILLY..

I'LL BUY THAT..
GBTrudeau

NEED ANY MORE HELP ON YOUR TERM PAPER?
NO, THANKS. I'M NOT GOING TO FINISH IT. I DECIDED LAST NIGHT TO DROP OUT OF SCHOOL AND GO TO VIETNAM.

WHAT?..
I'M TALKING TO MY R.O.T.C. OFFICER TODAY. IF I'M ACCEPTED, I WON'T HAVE TO FINISH MY TERM PAPER!

IT'S SOMETHING I'VE BEEN PLANNING TO DO FOR A LONG TIME ANYWAY!.. WITH ANY LUCK, THIS TIME NEXT WEEK, WHILE THE REST OF YOU GUYS ARE SLAVING AWAY, I'LL BE WINGING MY WAY TO VIETNAM!

TO GET OUT OF A TERM PAPER?
PRETTY CRAFTY, HUH?
©B Trudeau

WELL, GOODBY OL' FRIEND! GOOD LUCK IN VIETNAM...
GOODBY, BERNIE. AND THANKS FOR YOUR ENCOURAGE-MENT. I'M GLAD AT LEAST SOME-BODY THINKS I'M DOING THE RIGHT THING...

LEAST I COULD DO. AFTER ALL, YOU ARE WHAT YOU ARE..
AND WHAT'S THAT?

WHY, A LUNATIC, OF COURSE..
OF COURSE.

FLY ME TO THE MOON...
TAKE CARE, BERNIE..
GBTrudeau

WELL, GOOD LUCK IN VIETNAM, OL' ROOMIE..
THANKS, MIKE.

I WISH YOU'D CHANGE YOUR MIND. YOU'RE GOING TO BE A BIG LOSS TO BOTH THE TEAM AND YOUR FRIENDS..

..ALMOST ALL THE GUYS WERE REALLY SAD TO LEARN YOU WERE GOING..
"ALMOST"?..
HEY, CAP'N! I HEARD THE GOOD NEWS!

HEY, PRIVATE, WE'VE GOT TO GET GOING...
RIGHT, CAPTAIN..

WELL.. DAD.. MOM... I'M OFF TO WAR..
OUR THOUGHTS GO WITH YOU, SON!

I'LL WRITE EVERY WEEK, O.K.? YOU'RE NOT TO WORRY ABOUT ME... WELL, SO LONG..
GOODBY, B.D..

TO THE 'NAM, CAP'N!
FOR APPLE PIE, SON!
MY BABY!

HI, THERE. MY NAME'S B.D.! I VOLUNTEERED!
MY NAME'S GEORGE. I WAS DRAFTED.
EXIT

WELL, DON'T FEEL BAD.. THE IMPORTANT THING IS THAT YOU'RE ON YOUR WAY TO VIETNAM!!
EXIT

BOY, AM I EXCITED! I HAVEN'T BEEN THIS EXCITED ABOUT A TRIP SINCE LAST YEAR WHEN I FLEW TO FORT LAUDERDALE!
EXIT
LOOK! RICE PADDIES!
EXIT

Dear Mom and Dad,
While I'm waiting for the next wave of Commies to attack, I thought I'd drop you a quick line.
U.S.

I arrived in Vietnam yesterday and I must say, I love it! I'm stationed at Firebase Bundy in the Delta and I've got my own bunker and machine gun!! Can you imagine?!
U.S.

BLAM!
ZING!
U.S.

BLAM!
Well, have to run now.. Much love, B.D.
BANG!
ZING!
ZING!
ZING!
RAT TAT
"8"
RAT-A-TAT TAT!
TAT-
U.S.
©GBTrudeau

SAY, GEORGE, HAVE I TOLD YOU ABOUT MY GIRL, BOOPSIE?
NOPE.

SHE'S A REAL DOLL, GEORGE. BRIGHT, TOO. AND A GREAT SENSE OF HUMOR! ... FOR INSTANCE, WHY DID THE MORON THROW HIS CLOCK OUT THE WINDOW?
WHY?

'CAUSE... HEE, HEE... HE WANTED TO SEE TIME FLY! HAW! HA, HA, HA!

THAT'S ONE OF HER JOKES..
SHE'S A RIOT.
GBTrudeau

YOU KNOW WHAT BOTHERS ME, B.D.?– IT'S IMPOSSIBLE TO SEE THE ENEMY...
DON'T WORRY, GEORGE, HE'S OUT THERE..

AS A MATTER OF FACT, THERE'S CHARLIE NOW! BETTER GET DOWN, MAN...

ZING!
THAT'S ANOTHER THING! WHY DO WE ALWAYS CALL THE ENEMY "CHARLIE"? "CHARLIE" IS SUCH A BORING NAME!
ZING.
RAT TAT TAT

ZING!
WHY NOT "ARNOLD," OR "SEYMOUR," OR "PEABODY"?
YOU MEATHEAD.
RAT TAT TA
ZING!

BLAM!
ZING!
U.S.

HEY, YA LITTLE CREEP, WHAT'S THE BIG DEAL? I WAS EATING DINNER!! WHY DON'T YOU SHOW SOME RESPECT FOR THE AMERICAN FIGHTING MAN!?
U.S.

WHIZ!
PLOP!
U.S

KEEP IT UP, CHARLIE, JUST KEEP IT UP!
U.S.
GBTrudeau

GEORGE, WHAT'S GOING ON HERE? I'M TRYING TO GET SOME SLEEP...
BLAM!
ZING!
BLAM!
ZING!
BLAM!
V.C. GUNNER, B.D. !!

PESKY COMMIE!
BLAM!

AARRGGH! A TOUCH, I DO CONFESS IT! I FEAR I BREATHE MY LAST!
NOW WAIT A MINUTE...
HEE, HEE!
GBTrudeau

Vwwwwoooo
SIR, WE HAVE MET CHARLIE AND HE IS OURS.
GOT A BODY COUNT, CAP'N?

Vwwwwoooo
PRIVATE, WHAT DAY IS IT?

AH, FEBRUARY FIFTEENTH SIR...

FIFTEEN ENEMY DEAD, SIR.

I CAN'T BELIEVE IT! I'M LOST!

MY FIRST WEEK IN VIETNAM, AND I'M ALREADY MISSING IN ACTION!.. I'LL PROBABLY STARVE.. OR GET EATEN, EVEN!

HOWEVER!!.. EVEN IF I'M DESTINED TO DIE IN THIS CURSED JUNGLE, I STILL BELIEVE THIS WAR IS RIGHT, HONORABLE, AND A CREDIT TO AMERICA!

VELY NICE. HOW DO YOU FEEL ABOUT THE P.O.W. ISSUE?
GBTrudeau

WHADDA YA LOWERING YOUR GUN FOR, CHARLIE? SCARED OF ME?
NO. WE'RE LOST..

LOST? YOU'RE JOKING..
NO, I'M NOT- WE'RE LOST. LEND ME YOUR JUNGLE MAP AND I'LL SEE IF I CAN FIGURE OUT WHERE WE ARE..

AHA!
WHAT?
WE'RE LOST.
YOU SAID THAT.
©GBTrudeau

HEY, CHARLIE. HOW'D YOU COME TO LEARN ENGLISH?...
WHAT DO YOU MEAN? ENGLISH IS PRACTICALLY THE NATIONAL LANGUAGE IN VIETNAM.

IN CASE YOU DIDN'T KNOW, YOU RUNNING DOGS HAVE BEEN OCCUPYING OUR COUNTRY FOR FIFTEEN YEARS.. AND BY THE WAY, MY NAME'S PHRED, NOT CHARLIE...

I'M A V.C. TERRORIST. AND I'M A GOOD ONE, TOO! AIN'T NOBODY IN THESE PARTS WHO AIN'T HEARD OF "PHRED THE TERRORIST."

YESSIR, I CAN RAZE A HAMLET IN THIRTY SECONDS FLAT...
"PHRED THE TERRORIST."
©GBTrudeau

PHRED, I'VE BEEN THINKING..
BIG DEAL..

I'VE DECIDED TO FACE THE FACTS! WE'RE BOTH LOST AND HUNGRY, SO WE MIGHT AS WELL BE FRIENDS AND TRY TO MAKE IT TOGETHER.

EVEN THOUGH YOU'RE A COMMIE, I THINK IT WOULD BE WORTH-WHILE AND INSPIRATIONAL TO REALLY GET TO KNOW YOU..

ALSO, I COULDN'T HELP NOTICING YOUR CAN OF RICE.
©B Trudeau

PHRED, HOW COME YOU DECIDED TO BECOME A TERRORIST?..
HMM.. NOT SURE, REALLY, B.D...

PROBABLY BECAUSE MY FATHER WAS ONE. HE USED TO DO QUITE A JOB ON THE LOCAL FRENCH OUTPOSTS. DAD TAUGHT ME EVERYTHING I KNOW.

BUT WHAT WILL YOU DO WHEN THE WAR ENDS?..
NO SWEAT, JOE. IT'LL NEVER END! WE TERRORISTS HAVE THE MOST SECURE JOBS IN VIETNAM...

I'VE EVEN GOT A TEN YEAR CONTRACT.
©GBTrudeau

SIGH
Z-Z-Z

SLEEP ON, CHARLIE. YOU MAY BE LOST, BUT AT LEAST YOU'RE IN THE RIGHT COUNTRY.

ME, I'M THOUSANDS OF MILES FROM HOME, HUNGRY, TIRED, DISGRACED AND HUMILIATED. HOW COULD THINGS POSSIBLY GET ANY WORSE FOR ME?

Dear John...
GBTrudeau

SIGH... I SURE AM HUNGRY.. WHAT I'D GIVE FOR A BOWL OF RICE..

...ESPECIALLY MY MOTHER'S RICE! BOY, CAN SHE WHIP UP A MEAN BOWL OF RICE... YOU KNOW, I BET SHE'S WORRIED SICK ABOUT ME. I'VE NEVER LEFT HER ALONE THIS LONG..

AMAZING..
..I DIDN'T KNOW COMMIES HAD MOTHERS.
GBTrudeau

WELL, HERE WE ARE, DEEP IN THE HEART OF THE DELTA JUNGLE, HUDDLED AROUND A FIRE AS IF OUR VERY LIVES DEPEND UPON IT, WHICH IN FACT THEY DO.

RIGHT YOU ARE, PHRED! IF IT WEREN'T FOR THIS WARM, FRIENDLY FIRE TO SCARE OFF WILD BEASTS, THE STORY OF OUR VALIANT STRUGGLE FOR SURVIVAL MIGHT HAVE BEEN A SHORT ONE..

I WISH WE HAD SOME MARSHMALLOWS.

B.D., I KNOW HOW HARD IT MUST BE FOR YOU TO ACCEPT ME, WHAT WITH OUR DIFFERENT BACKGROUNDS AND ALL. I REALIZE HOW YOU FEEL..

YOU KNOW, I EVEN KNOW WHAT YOU'D LIKE TO CALL ME.. BUT YOU HAVEN'T SAID IT, ON ACCOUNT OF OUR JOINT STRUGGLE FOR SURVIVAL. BUT I WOULDN'T MIND REALLY.. GO AHEAD AND SAY IT..
O.K.

YOU LOUSY COMMIE GOOK!

THERE NOW, DON'T YOU FEEL BETTER?
YES, I NEEDED THAT..

GOOD EVENING. AS WE ALL KNOW, THE PRESIDENT HAS LEFT FOR AN EXCITING TRIP TO RED CHINA...

BEHIND HIM, HE HAS LEFT HIS NUMBER TWO MAN, SPIRO AGNEW, IN COMPLETE CONTROL OF THE COUNTRY...

WE ARE FORTUNATE TO HAVE MR. AGNEW HERE TONIGHT IN OUR STUDIO, AND HE'LL NOW SAY A FEW WORDS...

O.K., YOU SNOBS, THE PICNIC'S OVER...
GBTrudeau

WHAT EXACTLY ARE WE LOOKING FOR, PHRED?
A CACHE OF SUPPLIES MY MEN HID IN THIS AREA..

HEY, HERE IT IS! IT'S A BOX WE STOLE FROM THE U.S. SUPPLY DEPOT LAST MONTH..
WHAT?

WHAT'S IN IT?
DON'T KNOW. WE WERE DISCOVERED AND HAD TO LEAVE IT BEHIND...
©B Trudeau

BEER!
"SCHLITZ"?

"DEAR GUYS, WELL, HERE I AM IN VIETNAM, AND BELIEVE ME, IT'S NO PICNIC!"

"THIS IS A DIRTY, ROTTEN, STINKING WAR, BUT I LOVE IT! EVEN STILL, I SPEND EVERY NIGHT IN FEAR, NOT KNOWING IF IT WILL BE MY LAST.."

MAN, IT GIVES ME SHIVERS READING THIS LETTER, MARK. JUST THINK OF THE ADVENTURES OL' B.D. MUST BE EXPERIENCING RIGHT NOW..
© B Trudeau

BEER
GIN!
NUTS..

B.D.!
GEORGE!
GEORGE?

B.D., WE'VE BEEN LOOKING FOR YOU FOR A WEEK!
I GOT LOST ON PATROL, GEORGE. LUCKILY, I MET PHRED HERE, WHO IS A V.C. TERRORIST, AND HE SAVED US BY FINDING A CACHE OF SCHLITZ!
HIC

NOW LET ME GET THIS STRAIGHT...
HIC
©GBTrudeau

PRIVATE, I UNDERSTAND YOU INJURED YOUR HAND WHILE LOST OUT IN THE TEEMING VIETNAM JUNGLES.

TO HONOR SAID INJURY, I AWARD YOU THE PURPLE HEART! CONGRATULATIONS!
AH, YESSIR.

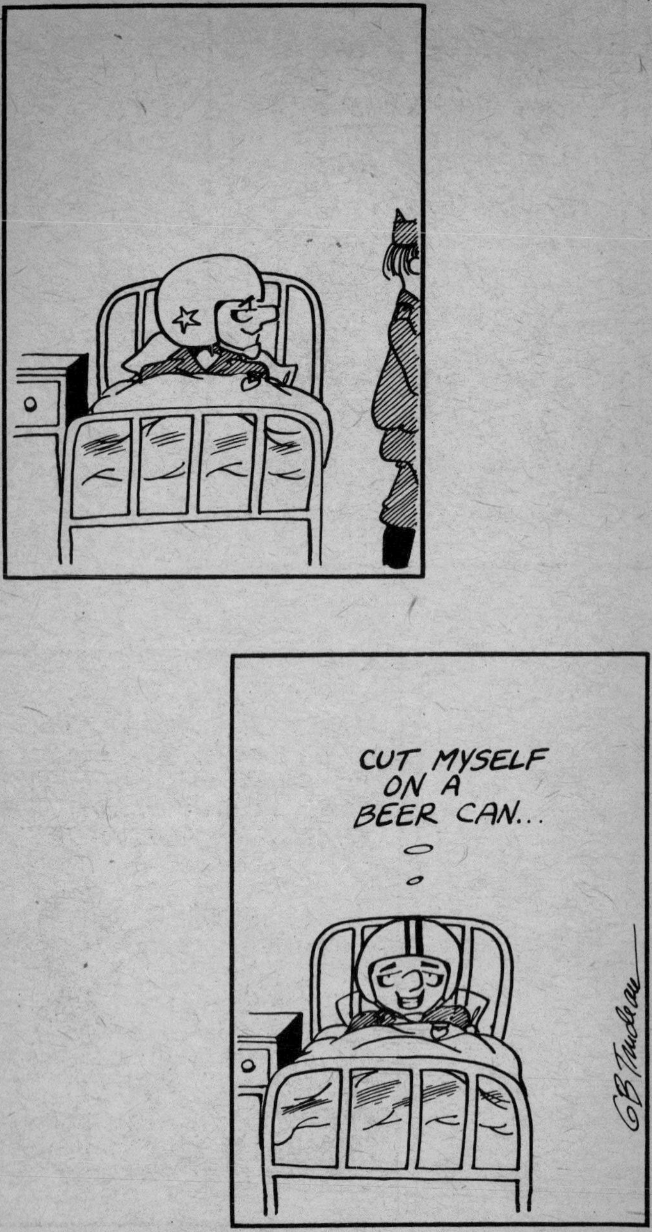
CUT MYSELF ON A BEER CAN...
GBTrudeau

WOW! LOOK, GEORGE! IT'S A SCORE OF PHANTOM JETS OFF ON A PROTECTIVE REACTION RAID!

MAN, JUST LOOK AT THEM SCREAM ACROSS THE SKY! WHAT COULD BE MORE DELICATE AND BEAUTIFUL IN FLIGHT THAN A PHANTOM JET?

BRAVO FOR LIFE'S LITTLE IRONIES.

HEY, CHARLIE! YOUR MOTHER WEARS COMBAT BOOTS!

BLAM! BLAM!
BLAM!

NYAH, NYAH! YA MISSED!

HA, HA! HA! HEE, HEE!
BEEN SMOKING A LITTLE SOMETHING, HAVE WE, PRIVATE?

B.D...I CAN'T UNDERSTAND HOW YOU OF ALL PEOPLE BECAME FRIENDS WITH PHRED! I THOUGHT YOU HATED COMMUNISTS.

I STILL DO! WITH A PASSION! BUT YOU CAN'T JUST IGNORE THE FACT HE SAVED MY LIFE. BESIDES, UNLIKE OTHER COMMIES, HE HAPPENS TO BE AN OKAY GUY.

YEAH, BUT IF HE'S SUCH A NICE GUY, WHY'D HE BECOME A TERRORIST?
WELL, IT WASN'T REALLY HIS FAULT...
HIS FAMILY PRESSURED HIM INTO IT...
GBTrudeau

HA! HA! YEA! TERRIFIC! ENCORE! ENCORE!
CLAP CLAP

HEE, HEE!.. BOY, WAS THAT A GREAT SHOW! THINK I'LL GET HIS AUTOGRAPH!

©GBTrudeau
GOT IT.
Best,
Bob Hope

HEAR ABOUT THE BOMBING RAID LAST NIGHT?.. 2,300 TONS!

THAT WASN'T A BOMBING RAID! IT WAS A PROTECTIVE REACTION STRIKE!

B.D., THEY DROP BOMBS IN BOTH CASES. THERE'S NO DIFFERENCE.
THERE'S A BIG DIFFERENCE, FELLAH!

A PROTECTIVE REACTION STRIKE MEANS NOT HAVING TO SAY YOU'RE SORRY.
GBTrudeau

DID I TELL YOU I'M THINKING OF CHANGING MY NAME?
WHATEVER FOR? WHAT'S WRONG WITH "RUFUS"?

WELL.. IT'S A LITTLE TRITE. EVERY OTHER KID ON MY BLOCK IS CALLED "RUFUS." I GUESS IT'S A CULTURAL THING...

ANYWAY, I'VE DECIDED TO GET ANOTHER NAME.. I THINK I WANT A NAME THAT REFLECTS MY ENORMOUS STRENGTH OF CHARACTER...
GOT ONE YET?

HOW DOES "THOR" GRAB YOU?
GBTrudeau

O.K., THOR, I'VE GOT A TOUGH ONE FOR YOU... WHAT'S THE SQUARE ROOT OF 144?

ELEVEN.
UH... NO, NOT QUITE. ELEVEN IS THE SQUARE ROOT OF 121. TRY AGAIN.

ELEVEN!
NO, MAN, I TOLD YOU-ELEVEN'S THE SQUARE ROOT OF 121! SO IT CAN'T BE ELEVEN, O.K.?

THOR HAS SPOKEN!
ELEVEN IT IS.
GBTrudeau

SOUNDS GOOD, GUYS! I, THOR, WILL BE OUT AFTER MY LESSON, O.K.?
WELL, HURRY UP, THOR!
YEAH, THE GUYS ARE WAITING.

I'M PITCHING, GOT IT?
NOW WAIT A MINUTE! JIM HERE'S GONNA PITCH..
YEAH, WHY SHOULD YOU PITCH?

BECAUSE IF THOR DOESN'T PITCH, HEADS ARE GOING TO ROLL!

THOR HAS SPOKEN!
ALL POWER TO THOR!

WHAT CAN I DO FOR YOU, ZONKER?
WELL, MIKE, I'M THINKING I'D LIKE TO WORK FOR THE PAPER.
TAP TAP
TAP

WORK FOR THE PAPER? ZONKER, WHAT DO YOU KNOW ABOUT REPORTING?
LOTS! LISTEN TO THIS!

HOT TYPE! SOFT NEWS! U.P.I..! EXTRA! SCOTTY RESTON! WIRE SERVICES! IN-DEPTH PROFILES!

SCOOP! PIX! PUT 'ER TO BED, BOYS!
OKAY, OKAY..
TAP TAP

PATRONAGE JOBS?..THAT'S A PRETTY SERIOUS THING TO ACCUSE PRESIDENT KING OF..
WELL, THAT'S WHAT I HEARD. AS INVESTIGATIVE REPORTERS, I THINK WE OUGHT TO LOOK INTO IT.

AFTERNOON. WE'RE FROM THE CAMPUS NEWS. IS THE PRESIDENT IN?
UH-HUH, YOU'RE EXPECTED.

THE BOYS FROM THE NEWS ARE HERE, DAD.

I THINK WE MAY BE ON TO SOMETHING..
GBTrudeau

ZONKER, I MUST CONGRATULATE YOU ON YOUR PRESIDENT KING EXPOSÉ! THE LETTERS HAVE BEEN POURING IN!

I'M ESPECIALLY OVERWHELMED BY YOUR EVIDENCE! DATES, FIGURES, NAMES— WHEREVER DID YOU DIG UP ALL THESE FACTS?!

I MADE THEM UP.

PRETTY TRICKY, HUH?
©BTrudeau

RING! RING!
TAP TAP

NEWS. ... AH, RIGHT. YEAH, I KNOW ABOUT IT, HERBIE.
GBTrudeau

YES, HERBIE, I KNOW ABOUT THE RIOT. ..HEY, DON'T WORRY, HERB, I KNOW IT'S IMPORTANT. I HAVE MY BEST MAN ON IT RIGHT NOW.

HELLO. MY NAME'S JIMMY OLSEN.

ZONKER?!
TAP
TAP

HEY, MIKE, SEEN ZONKER?
DIDN'T YOU HEAR? HE LEFT EARLY YESTERDAY MORNING ON AN ASSIGNMENT.

WHAT ASSIGNMENT?
HE GOT A UNIVERSITY GRANT TO SPEND SPRING VACATION IN SOUTH-EAST ASIA! HE'S GOING TO BE OUR WAR CORRESPONDENT.

SURPRISED, CAP'N?
PRESS
GBTrudeau

March 16 - It's a hot, humid day here on Firebase Bundy. The brave private, B.D., sits by his machine gun, taking a brief respite - a "breather," in G.I. jargon - between enemy onslaughts, which he must, and does, repel at the daily risk of his life.

BLAM!
ZING!

AHA! A CALL TO ARMS!
©GBTrudeau

TAT-TAT
RAT-TAT
TAT
TAT
TAT
Nonetheless, he does seem to enjoy his work.

SAY, DID YOU GUYS HEAR THAT THE PRESIDENT SAID THAT THE BOYS IN THE 'NAM ARE IN DEFENSIVE POSTURES?
RIGHT!
PRESS
PRETTY FAR OUT DEFENSIVE POSTURES!
BOY, DOES THAT MAN JIVE! HE SURE DOESN'T KNOW MUCH ABOUT WHAT'S GOING ON OVER HERE.
PRESS

WHAT A FOOLISH HOMBRE!
I'LL SAY! WHY'D YA SUPPOSE PEOPLE VOTE FOR HIM?
PRESS

HE KNOWS HOW TO HANDLE PUNKS LIKE YOU.
PRESS
GBTrudeau

IT'S ANOTHER HOT DAY HERE AT FIREBASE BUNDY AS B.D. MANS HIS POST WITH FORTITUDE AND BRAVADO.
BLAM! BLAM!
RAT-A-TAT-TAT.
TAT!

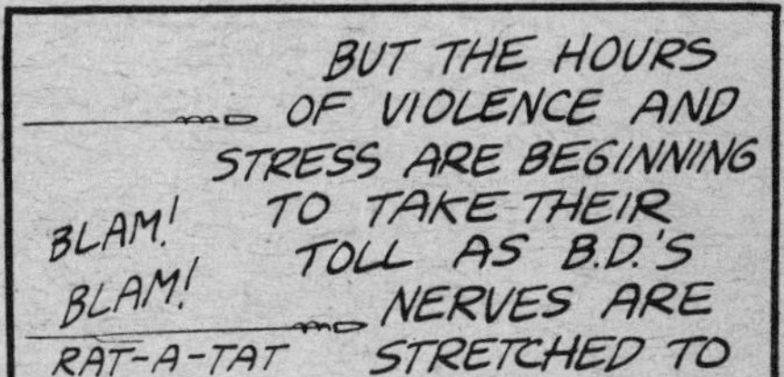
BUT THE HOURS OF VIOLENCE AND STRESS ARE BEGINNING TO TAKE THEIR TOLL AS B.D.'S NERVES ARE STRETCHED TO THE BREAKING POINT... TENSE... NERVOUS..
BLAM! BLAM!
RAT-A-TAT TAT
TAT

WILL YA SHADDUP!

YES, DEAR READERS, HE'S BEGINNING TO BREAK..

HEY, CAP'N! WE IN SAIGON YET?
NO, DUMMY, OF COURSE NOT! THESE'RE THE OUTSKIRTS!
PRESS

WELL, LOOK, MAN, I'VE GOTTA GET PIX OF THE CITY. SO TELL ME WHEN WE'RE IN SAIGON PROPER.
PRESS

PRESS
©BTrudeau

WE'RE IN SAIGON PROPER.
PRESS

NOW DON'T BLOW THIS INTERVIEW, CAP'N. IT TOOK A LOT OF HASSLE TO INTEREST THESE T.V. DUDES IN YOU...
YEAH, YEAH.. LET'S GET IT OVER WITH.
PRESS

THIS IS ZONKER HARRIS, SPECIAL STUDENT WAR CORRESPONDENT IN SAIGON. TODAY I'M RAPPING WITH A FAMOUS EX-COLLEGE QUARTER-BACK, WHO AFTER SIX WEEKS IN VIETNAM, HAS A VERY UNUSUAL OPINION ABOUT THE WAR.

I LOVE IT.
PRESS

ZONKER HARRIS, SAIGON.
GBTrudeau

I'M READY, PROFESSOR! AND SO'S MY FORMULA.
WELL, PROCEED, BERNIE. I'M ANXIOUS TO SEE THIS WEREWOLF FORMULA OF YOURS.

WELL?
HMM.. NOT BAD, NOT BAD. BUT THE HAIR'S A LITTLE COARSE, AND THE EARS A LITTLE SMALL.. ..HMMM.... 78!

78?

HE WORKED VERY HARD ON HIS WEREWOLF FORMULA.
SOB!
BOO HOO!

MIKE, I CAN'T UNDERSTAND WHY I DID SO POORLY ON MY WEREWOLF TEST YESTERDAY.
WELL, BERNIE, MAYBE YOUR PROFESSOR JUST HAS A BIAS AGAINST WEREWOLVES.

YES, YES, THAT'S PROBABLY IT, MIKE! THE REASON HE GAVE ME SUCH A BAD GRADE IS THAT HE'S A BIGOT! LIKE MANY PEOPLE, HE HATES WEREWOLVES!

BUT THINGS ARE GOING TO CHANGE, MIKE! YOU'LL SEE! MY FORMULA IS JUST THE BEGINNING! I SEE A DAY WHEN WEREWOLVES WILL BE ACCEPTED! YES, I SEE A DAY WHEN THEY WILL BE ADMIRED AND RESPECTED!

I SEE A DAY WHEN YOU'RE PUT AWAY.